CARL NIELSEN
HUMOROUS BAGATELLES

Op.11

THE ASSOCIATED BOARD OF
THE ROYAL SCHOOLS OF MUSIC

INTRODUCTION

Carl Nielsen (1865-1931) is considered to be the finest composer that Denmark has produced. He was born, the seventh of twelve children, in a small Danish village to a painter in humble circumstances. At an early age he displayed musical talent, and he was encouraged in this by his parents. He learned the violin, playing in his father's village band, and he delighted in imitating his mother's singing and improvising variations on dance tunes. At the age of fifteen he joined a military orchestra, playing the horn and trombone, and four years later he entered the Copenhagen Conservatory. After completing his studies, he remained in Copenhagen for the rest of his life, working first of all as a violinist in the royal chapel and, when he was better established, as a composer, conductor and teacher.

His compositions are quite extensive. Best known for the six symphonies, he also wrote for various chamber and instrumental groups, for the stage, and for choirs and solo voices. His style was noticeably different from the Romantic music of his time and to some extent looked back to the Classical idiom. But he was in no way a traditionalist. His composition, based on the essential twin elements of melody and rhythm derived from his early experience of village music-making, owes little to any antecedents and still remains today highly individualistic.

The six *Humorous Bagatelles*, written in 1894-7, are among his most charming works for piano and clearly reflect Nielsen's simple melodic and rhythmic style. In the present edition, a few pedal markings have been added, one or two minor misprints corrected, and some of the fingering revised. The metronome setting at the end of each piece is only a suggestion and should in no way be regarded as authoritative.

Good Morning! Good Morning!

NIELSEN, Op. 11

The Top

A little slow Waltz

Jumping Jack

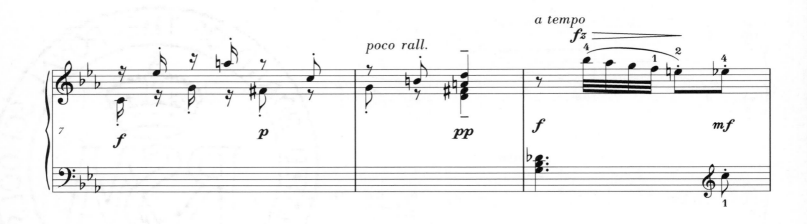

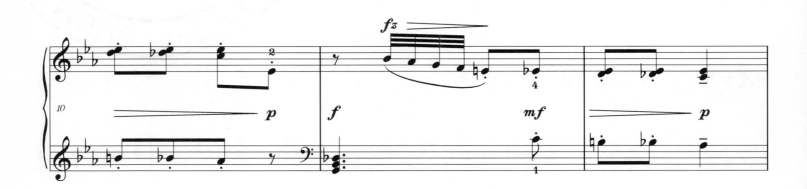

[♩ = c. 100]

Doll's March

release
carefully

release carefully

[♩ = c. 126]

The Musical Clock

Allegretto scherzando

[♩ = c. 92]

AB 1882

Reproduced and printed by
Halstan & Co. Ltd., Amersham, Bucks., England